I dedicate this book to my children, Arian and Adyn, who I hope always reach for the stars.

-Reetu

www.mascotbooks.com

Ari Loves the Solar System

©2014 Reetu Dua. All Rights Reserved. No part of this publication may
be reproduced, stored in a retrieval system or transmitted in any form
by any means electronic, mechanical, or photocopying, recording or
otherwise without the permission of the author.

For more information, please contact:
Mascot Books
560 Herndon Parkway #120
Herndon, VA 20170
info@mascotbooks.com

Library of Congress Control Number: 2014918267

CPSIA Code: PRT1214A
ISBN-13: 978-1-62086-994-9

Printed in the United States

Ari Loves the Solar System

Reetu Dua

illustrated by Tina Modugno

The Sun

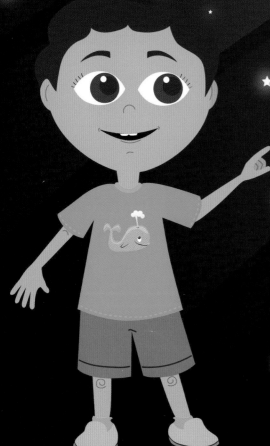

Ari loves the sun,
It's so yellow and bright.
It's the center of the solar system,
And gives us so much light!

The sun is a huge star
Way up in the sky.
It's so hot and really far,
It gives us life, oh my!

MERCURY

The first planet is Mercury,
It's very small and gray.
As we shoot through the galaxy,
Ari says, "What a great day!"

Mercury is closest to the sun.
It is a ball of iron and dust.
The universe is so fun,
Learning about it is a must!

VENUS

Venus is the second planet,
It's very hot and yellow.
Ari wonders if there is life on it
As he catches its beautiful glow.

Ari sees a crater,
He wonders what's inside.
He learns there's no life or water!
What's next on this Solar System ride?

EARTH

Earth is the third planet from the sun,
It has a beautiful moon.
Ari's having so much fun,
He sees the green and blue!

Earth has water and land,
And many stars to look up to.
On this planet, Ari stands
And hopes to protect it too.

Protect
The
Earth

Mars is planet number four
It has rocks and ice caps.
Ari wants to see more
As he looks at his solar system map.

Mars is dark red,
And has the tallest mountain.
Ari stares at it from his bed
And dreams about seeing it again.

The fifth planet is Jupiter.
Ari sees a big red spot.
Some gas and liquid matter,
Wow, is that an astronaut?

Jupiter is the biggest planet
And has so many moons.
Ari knows it spins the fastest,
He'll see it someday soon.

The sixth planet is Saturn,
Ari loves its beautiful rings.
He uses his telescope to learn
About the universe and things.

Saturn looks light yellow,
And it's mostly made of gas.
Ari sees its nice glow
In his astronomy class.

URANUS

The seventh planet is Uranus,
It's light blue and very cold.
Ari sees many craters,
There are many moons, he is told.

Ari sees rings made of dust,
He is overjoyed!
Uranus has a rocky crust.
Is that an asteroid?

NEPTUNE

The eighth planet is Neptune,
It's so gorgeous and blue.
Ari hopes to see it soon
To see if it's all true.

Neptune has a lot of ice,
Because the sun is so far away.
Its storm doesn't look so nice,
Ari will visit it another day!

Let's review the solar system with Ari!

Neptune

Earth

Saturn

Mars

Mercury

Jupiter

The Sun

Venus

Uranus

About the Author

After the success of her first book, *Ari Loves the Holidays*, Reetu Dua decided to write about another one of her children's passions—the Solar System. Reetu is the proud mother of two sons, Arian and Adyn. Both kids have been mesmerized by the magnificence of the wonders of the universe including the Sun, planets, stars, and moon. Through her children's exuberance for learning, Reetu has penned a book that not only engages children to learn about the colors, sizes, shapes, and objects that make up our universe, but also expands children's imagination and penchant for learning about our place in this world.

Reetu is the creator of the *Ari Loves* series, an innovative set of books designed to teach children in new and interesting ways.